Treat the Earth well.
It was not given to us by our parents;
it was loaned to us by our children.

*Ancient Proverb*

*For Isabella Andrea Grace* ~ C F

*For my grandmother, Tess Macnaughton* ~ T M

This edition published by Scholastic Inc., 557 Broadway; New York, NY 10012,
by arrangement with Little Tiger Press.
SCHOLASTIC and associated logos are trademarks and/or
registered trademarks of Scholastic Inc.
Distributed by Scholastic Canada Ltd; Markham, Ontario

Original edition published in English by LITTLE TIGER PRESS,
an imprint of Magi Publications, London, England, 2009

Text copyright © Claire Freedman 2009
Illustrations copyright © Tina Macnaughton 2009

ISBN-10: 1-84895-017-9
ISBN-13: 978-1-84895-017-7

Printed in China

1 3 5 7 9 10 8 6 4 2

# Where Snowflakes Fall

Claire Freedman          Tina Macnaughton

The glittering, icy world wakes up to the sun.
In this fragile white land, a new day's begun.

Snow leopards wake to the pink blush of dawn,
still drowsy from sleep, they're cozy and warm.

Perched on the cliffs where it's craggy and steep,
hungry for breakfast, the puffin chicks cheep.

Far, far below, where the sea meets the shore,
foamy white waves crash the rocks with a roar.

From deep in their den, polar bears tumble out.
On wobbly paws, they wiggle about.

Full of excitement, they run and they chase
in this most precious and beautiful place.

Baby whale glides through the crystal blue sea.
In the calm waters, he's happy and free.

Close to his mother's side, diving together,
down in the ocean that stretches forever.

Icicles glisten and glint in the light,
long, slender crystals that sparkle so bright.

Drawn from their cave by the first rays of sun,
lively young lemmings dart out to have fun.

Blue-shadowed snowfields lie still and serene,
here where the air is so pure and so clean.

Sheltered by mountains, the caribou deer
rest by the stream, flowing icy and clear.

Ready to explore, the small Arctic fox
peeks from his lair in the snow-sparkled rocks.

Eyes full of wonder, he can't wait to go,
nimble and light as the soft, swirling snow.

Wings tipped with sunshine, the snow geese glide by.
They gracefully soar through the endless blue sky.

Wrapped in his mother's wings, sheltered and still,
warm through the blizzard and harsh, bitter chill.

Soft shadows fall as the sun slips away.
Snowy white clouds turn to purple and gray.

Arctic hares hop home, all tired and dozy.
Soon they'll be sleeping and cuddled up cozy.

The northern lights shimmer and dance up on high.
Majestically, snowy owl swoops through the sky.

Over the magical ice-world he flies,
and only the moon hears his soft, haunting cries.

Little seal lies in his mother's warm cuddle.
In the cold stillness, together they huddle.

The frosty land sparkles with the softest starlight.
Sleep, precious ice-world, sleep safely tonight.